TRES CASAS TRES FAMILIAS

by Edna Beiler

FRIENDSHIP PRESS   *NEW YORK*

*To Johnny Beck and his parents
in appreciation of their
warm friendliness and
spontaneous kindness*

Contents

1 Casa Santero

¡ENTRE!

That is the Spanish word for *come in*.

In this book there are three Spanish Americans who are saying that to you. Benito—Juan—Felisa. All of them are waiting for you, in the stories in this book.

They are saying *"¡Entre!"* so that you may step into their lives for a few days and see what they are doing. They invite you into their *casas,* homes, to visit their families. They will tell you their problems, their hopes, their secret longings to know you better and do all the things you do in your everyday life. By knowing them you will surely understand all Spanish Americans a little better. They may even help you understand yourself a little better, too!

Benito Santero lived in Cuba. His father was a doctor. Benito was proud of the skill in his father's slender hands, as he operated. Benito loved the bright, sunny little country of Cuba, where a man must have special permission to cut down a palm tree because they are so valuable and beautiful. He loved the streets of his own town. Especially, he loved his American friend, Michael.

For Benito, as for so many of his countrymen, all of this was changed almost overnight. You already know about the revolution in Cuba. The democratic ideals of the revolutionary fighters, such as freedom of speech and freedom of worship, were supported by the Cuban people. However, the government leaders began to move away from these ideals, and finally they rejected them altogether. Cubans who did not agree with the government came under suspicion.

Most Cubans who have fled to the United States have come by plane, but many of those who are under suspicion cannot get the papers they need. So they must come secretly, by boat.

The story of Benito and his family is a true story (although the names are fictional). The Santero family's escape by boat was more fortunate than hundreds of others who suffered unbelievable hardships. One man who works with Church World Service, an organization that helps people in need all over the world, knows many real-life stories. He says, "One day, I talked with five young men who rowed across in an eight-foot rowboat! They were picked up about twenty miles from Key West. I could tell you stories about people being killed while trying to escape. Twenty-four people were adrift in a twenty-eight-foot board for more than a week, after the motor gave out. One group spent four days on a fifty-foot rock, washed by waves."

Even coming by plane is an ordeal. It takes so many months to get emigration papers that sometimes people give up hope of ever getting them. In fact, they cannot be sure they will be able to leave until they are on the plane, enroute to Miami.

Cubans who come to Miami usually want to stay there. Everyone in Miami seems to understand Spanish. The stores carry Cuban foods. If they go elsewhere, they will have to buy foods that the mother of the family does not know how to cook. Their homes and their possessions are gone; of course, they want to stay at a place that seems familiar and is close to Cuba.

During 1963, an average of 360 Cubans were registering with Church World Service in Miami every week. They cannot all stay there. That is why Church World Service workers are trying so hard to help thousands, like Benito's family, to resettle elsewhere in North America.

You will want to watch the newspapers and TV programs to keep informed about what Cuban refugees are doing. It may be that your own church congregation (either alone or with several others) is sponsoring the re-settlement of a refugee family. If so, you will want to think about what you can do to make them feel at home.

The Butterfly Kite

Benito Santero bent over his work bench in the little back room beyond their kitchen. Outside, the Cuban sunshine lay bright over the patio and garden, but he paid no attention to it.

Carefully, Benito shaped the little piece of purple tissue paper. Then he lifted the frame of the half-finished kite he was making and put on a daub of glue. Finally, he settled the scrap of paper in place.

It seemed to fit neatly. Yet, when Benito stepped back to inspect the effect, he frowned.

"It's good enough, I suppose," he muttered to himself. "But it's not the same—making a kite all by myself. I wish Michael were here."

That was the way with so many things now, Benito thought to himself. When Michael Reed and his family had lived in the house on the corner, Benito hardly knew what loneliness was. He and Michael liked doing things with their hands. They had good times roaming the banks of the Sagua la Grande River, where it cut their town— also Sagua la Grande—neatly in two before winding its way to the sea at la Isabel.

Benito remembered how strange Michael had felt when the Reeds first came to Cuba from the United States. Yet, even during those first days when he couldn't speak Spanish, Michael found everyday things at Sagua la Grande exciting.

It was that more than anything else that drew the two boys together. Benito explained things and Michael listened. Benito told Michael what the tamale man was shouting as he walked down the street, and explained the words the boy selling brooms yodeled at the front doorstep.

They visited the Hernandez café with its big doors open to the sidewalk and bought three ice cream cones, one each for themselves and one for Peter, the green and gold parrot. Peter always accepted it solemnly, croaked a gruff, "Thank you!" clutched it in one claw, and began to eat.

The two boys sat on benches in the shadow of the church in the square and watched the *coches* pull up alongside. Michael had liked the little horse-drawn carriages that took people all over the city, but Benito admired his father's own sleek, big Cadillac more.

Once, they had even been allowed to take the short train trip to la Isabel together. They had visited Doña Miranda in her little house, built on piles over the water, with a boardwalk leading out to it. Doña Miranda was old and ill now, but she had been kind to Papa Santero when he was a boy.

Afterwards, that bright day always stayed in Benito's mind like a little picture. The seaport town, drenched in Cuban sunshine, the white gulls flying over the square, and the big ships loading at the docks—all were part of the picture. But best of all was the fact that the two of them had traveled to la Isabel together. He and Michael were *friends*.

But now that the Reeds were gone—well, Benito found himself thinking about them from morning to night. The Reeds had stayed all during the difficult days of the Revolution. In spite of the fighting, Señor Reed had kept right on grading papers from the Bible course he taught by correspondence. His little office was filled with lessons with red pencil marks on them, stacked here and there, ready to put into the mail. Some of his students lived on nearby islands like Haiti and Puerto Rico. But there came a day—

Benito sighed suddenly. Everyone had hoped for so much from the Revolution. There had been bad times at first, of course; he shuddered to think about them even yet. But after that, there was hope in the very air they breathed—hope that seemed to make the sunshine brighter, the towering palm trees more majestic, the very ripple of the waves along the curving white beaches of Cuba a promise of happier days to come.

Gradually, this hope and promise ebbed and trickled away. Slowly, so slowly that Benito could not say just when it started, a gray cloud began to settle over them all. And the sun seemed never to shine as brightly anymore.

Some people, like the Reeds, had to leave right away because they were no longer allowed to bring in money from the United States. But at least everyone knew where they were going and why. Later on, many people just disappeared; no one knew where. And because of the mystery of these goings, those who remained began to doubt and suspect their neighbors. They were careful in their conversations, even with their friends. If they knew people who had different opinions about the government and its leaders, they lived in fear.

And now that Michael was gone, the big butterfly kite they had started to build together had gathered dust on Benito's work bench, until now it was kite season, with bright, windy days once more. So Benito had decided to work on the kite by himself.

"Mer-ow!" A purring ball of fur wrapped itself around Benito's ankle.

"Why, Blanco!" Benito said. He lifted the white cat into his arms and leaned his face against the soft fur.

Blanco had come to them during the Revolution. Holding him tightly in his arms, Benito remembered that night—one of the worst they had had.

Their house had been locked tight, every shutter closed, so that not a breath of air could get in. Benito was too hot and too frightened to sleep. The night silence was stabbed by the sound of guns, as soldiers fought up and down the *Avenida,* holding the bridge that crossed the Sagua la Grande River.

The next morning, Papa went to the hospital across the river to see several patients; and he did not come back that night. Once, when Benito dared to look from an upstairs window for a moment, he had seen smoke from fires in half a dozen different places. He also saw the rebel flag flying from the church tower across the river while men swarmed along the parapet, as they guarded the bridge below.

The next night, it seemed to Benito that he could not breathe. Suddenly, he thought he heard a faint "Mer-ow."

Creeping out of bed, he groped his way to the big front door and peeked out.

"Mer-ow!"

Benito held his breath. Yes, there *was* a little cat perched on their doorstep. He felt as if he could see it, squeezed back against the step in terror. Perhaps its owners had gone elsewhere to live with relatives until the fighting was over. More likely the owners had gone visiting somewhere and could not return.

"Mer-ow!"

Benito leaned against the door. He wanted to rescue the poor little animal, but did he dare? What would Mama say if she knew? Yet the little cat was waiting.

He put his mouth close to the door jamb and breathed, "Kitty!"

"Mer-ow!" The answer was so confident, so full of hope that it gave Benito courage. Carefully he lifted the little chain on the inside of the door. Slowly he edged up the big bar and the door swung open an inch or two. Blanco streaked in and dived under a chair, while Benito dropped the bolt into place again.

Now, with Blanco purring in his arms, Benito knew that the Revolution had brought him at least one good thing.

"Benito!" Mama called and he came back to the present with a jolt. Dropping the cat, Benito returned to the cool, shadowy living room.

"What were you doing?" she asked.

"Working on the butterfly kite, Mama. But it is no fun without Michael."

Mama nodded sympathetically. At first, she had not approved of his friendship with Michael.

"We have our own way of worshiping God," she said, stiffly, when the Reeds moved into the house on the corner.

"But Tío Carlos over in Florida belongs to the Evangelical Church just as the Reeds do." Benito replied. *"Por favor,* do not say no, Mama."

It was true that the Reeds went to the little church on the other side of town instead of going to the big white church on the square where Benito, Carmen, Elena, and Mama went. But the Reeds never mentioned their church unless someone asked. They were kind and friendly without saying much about their faith. When Mama realized this, she relaxed and made friends with them, too.

"Mer-ow." Blanco had followed and was purring for a little attention.

Now Mama stroked Blanco, then took Benito's hand in hers. "Life has changed in so many ways for us all, Benito," she half whispered. "It gives me pain to think that

Cubans are fighting each other. But we must be brave—
because the trouble is not ended. We do not know what
will happen to us tomorrow—or even *today*."

"What could happen, Mama?" Benito asked. He had
heard so many half-hints from his parents lately—dark
phrases that made him shiver with fear, snatches of sentences that dropped off in the middle without an ending.
Benito could never quite piece them together afterwards.

"It is dreadful—dreadful," Papa would say to Mama
with a groan. "Why, Josefa, some people are settling old
grudges by filing false charges against people they don't
like. It gives me pain to think about it—"

"Sh! The children!" Mama would always reply. Then
they would change the subject quickly, but Benito had
heard enough.

Now, Mama still sat quietly, her eyes cast down, her
hands clasped tightly in her lap. Finally, she unclasped
them and lifted her head with a smile. She put one finger
under Benito's chin and tipped his face up so that his
eyes looked directly into hers.

"Son, I am going to ask you to do something brave
for Papa and me, but I cannot tell you the reason now. It
is better that you do not know some things just yet.
Then, if anyone asks, you will know nothing."

Her voice was so solemn now, that Benito felt queer prickles at the back of his neck. All the strange, half-said things he had heard during the past weeks seemed to be choking him.

"So much depends on you, Benito," Mama went on. "You do not understand, but you must believe me. Everything—perhaps even Papa's life—depends on you."

Benito swallowed hard and drew himself up tall. "I am strong, Mama. What is it you want me to do?"

They were both whispering, and now Mama leaned closer. "Go to the park now and get Elena and Carmen."

A minute ago, Benito had felt as if he were the butterfly kite, soaring high in the air. Now he felt as if he had fallen to earth and was flopping in the grass. Go to the park for his sisters! He had expected to do some big, heroic thing!

Mama was going on, so he had to forget his feelings and listen. "The three of you will start walking home—very slowly as if it were just any day. When you come to the *Avenida,* look carefully as you walk along, until you are sure there is no one around who knows you."

"Yes, Mama." Benito took heart. This was more like it.

"Then, turn down the little alley behind the Hernandez café. You know—Ramón Hernandez, Papa's friend?"

"Where Peter Parrot lives?"

"Yes, Benito. Go to the third door on the left side of the alley. Don't knock, just walk in. And wait there until Papa comes. No matter how long it is, wait without making a noise. If you can be brave and patient, we will all be safe by tomorrow. But if anything goes wrong, it may be very bad for Papa."

After that, Mama made Benito repeat her directions carefully, so that she was quite sure he knew them. Then she said, "And one more thing, my brave little son."

Benito stood waiting. He could hear his heart pounding in his chest. Mama leaned close to him, with her mouth at his ear.

"Be very careful as you pass Dr. Garcia's house. Walk slowly and whistle to yourself, as if you were happy and carefree. It is important that he should suspect nothing."

Benito nodded his head. He knew that Dr. Garcia had always despised his father.

"That's because everybody loves Papa—and he is a better doctor than Dr. Garcia!" his little sister Elena said, wisely.

But whatever the reason, Dr. Garcia had done many things in the past to hurt Papa's practice. Lately, he had said very little, but Benito shuddered whenever he saw Dr. Garcia get into his car with a contemptuous glance over his shoulder at the Santero house, down the street.

Often, there was a thin kind of half-smile on his lips as he drove away.

Now, Benito shivered a little. Was Dr. Garcia really such a bitter enemy that they had to leave Cuba because of him? Was Papa really in danger of being taken away from them forever?

"Mer-ow!" Blanco's voice at his ankle reassured him.

Quickly, Benito scooped Blanco into his arms and swept him under his jacket. Then, he went out through the big front room, with its carved chairs, that was the waiting room for Papa's patients. His mother followed him to the front doorstep.

"Go straight to the park for your little sisters," she told him. Her tones were firm, loud ones that would carry across the street.

"Yes, Mama," Benito called back over his shoulder as he started down the street.

Near the corner, he turned. Their own house, like those around them, had its front doorstep right on the sidewalk. The shutters were closed to keep out the glare of the late afternoon sunshine. A wisteria vine grew up over one corner and peeped in at the second story window.

As he approached the corner, Benito could see Dr. Garcia's house, too. It looked as innocent and homelike as his own, but back of the closed shutters lurked malice and hate.

"But we will soon be safe, *Dios mediante*," Benito whispered to himself as he walked on.

Benito remembered the day he had explained to Michael about that phrase. *"Dios mediante.* Everybody says that here in Cuba. It means 'If God wills it.' "

"Dios mediante." Michael had repeated the strange words over to himself softly. "I like that, Benito. It is a good reminder."

Benito looked doubtful. "We all say that, over and over," he said. "But I do not think we mean much by it. It is just a—how do you say it?—a saying, like 'how are you?' "

Now, as he walked toward the park, *Dios mediante* was no longer just an expression to Benito. Instead, it was a prayer to God to "will" his father to safety.

Benito hugged Blanco close and tried to walk in a slow, carefree way, as if this were any day—just any day at all. Yet Benito himself knew that he and Blanco were walking out of one life and stepping boldly into another.

Escape in the Night

Benito walked, as he had done hundreds of times before, down the *Avenida* to the city square. He cut across the bright cube of sunshine in the center of town and hurried on to the park.

That afternoon, the little park swarmed with children, and a few grownups, who were flying kites. A little four-year-old was trying to coax his "kite" into the air—just a scrap of paper tied to a string. Beyond him was a man with a beautiful big kite, made to look like a parrot. He was surrounded by a crowd of children.

"Be careful!" the man yelled. "Here I go!"

As the children scattered, he grabbed the kite and ran lightly across the grass. In a minute, the breeze caught the green and gold bird and carried it up and far away over the palms that lined the *Avenida*.

"It really does look like a live parrot, pulling on the

string like that," thought Benito as he stopped to watch. "Maybe it wants to be free—to fly high into the air. . . ."

"Were you looking for us, Benito?" His sister Elena stood at his elbow. She was holding Carmen's hand.

"Yes," Benito said. "Mama sent me, so we must go right away."

He was ashamed of himself. For that minute, while he was watching the parrot kite, he had forgotten everything else. He had forgotten how much depended on him. Now, he must make up for it by being as brisk and business-like as he could. He took Carmen's hand and motioned Elena to walk beside him.

"We will go this way—to the *Avenida*."

Something in the tone of his voice caught Elena's attention.

"What is it, Benito?" she asked urgently. The little crease in her forehead told how worried she was.

"Let's start walking and I will explain," he told her.

They walked down the street with Carmen bouncing along without paying much attention. Benito spoke to Elena over her head, telling her Mama's instruction.

"We will wait there until Papa comes for us," he said, in his most matter-of-fact voice. He talked that way because Elena's white face reflected exactly what he himself was feeling in the hollow of his stomach. But he did not tell her that. Elena was the serious one of their family; Mama said she took things too hard. Benito must be calm and brave for all three of them.

"But, Benito—suppose Papa does not come?" The words poured out in a whispered gasp.

Benito shook his head at Elena, as he glanced down at Carmen's dark curls, bobbing along between them.

"Papa *will* come," he said, stiffly.

They were at the alley now. Benito scarcely paused as he took one long look all around them. No one who might recognize them was near. Tomorrow, no one could say, "I saw the Santero children in the alley behind the Hernandez Café."

Quickly he turned down the alley, pulling Carmen along after him. Elena stumbled a little behind them. He counted the doors they passed—one, two, and at last, the third. A moment later, they had stepped inside.

The three children found themselves in a small storeroom with one high window that gave a greyish light. Together, they huddled down on a box in a far corner. Carmen whimpered a bit, but Benito unbuttoned his jacket and lifted Blanco over into his sister's lap.

Carmen petted Blanco as he settled down for another nap. In a few minutes, his purr changed from a loud roar to a steady low rumble.

"Good for Blanco!" Benito muttered to himself.

The little room was warm and quiet. Once, Carmen opened her mouth to speak, but Benito quickly clasped his hand over it. When she looked at him indignantly, he shook his head. Presently, she slumped over against him and he saw that she was fast asleep, too.

"I guess that's why Mama let her skip her *siesta,* her nap, this afternoon," Elena whispered.

Benito breathed a sigh of relief. Carmen was the *chiquita,* the youngest one, in their family—and she was spoiled by everyone. She liked having her own way and could scream lustily when she was determined to do something or when her feelings were hurt. Benito had been afraid of an outburst that might betray them all.

Elena was silent, but when she leaned her head against his shoulder Benito could feel her body tremble. For a moment, he thought she had gone to sleep, but when he looked closely, he saw that she was still staring into the shadows of the room.

The light from the little window gradually faded out entirely so that the storeroom was really dark before the door opened and a man entered.

"Papa?" The word was a question, barely breathed into the darkness.

"Yes," Papa said softly. "One little minute, Benito."

He turned to the inner door and knocked on it twice, just barely striking the wood with his knuckles. In a minute, the two soft little knocks were returned from the inside. Then he turned and picked up Carmen and Blanco.

"Come," he whispered.

Benito took Blanco and tucked him inside his jacket. Then he took Elena's hand and they followed their father outside. He knew that Papa and his friend had arranged a signal between them. Tomorrow, if anyone asked questions, Señor Hernandez could say, truthfully, "I did not see any of the Santero family yesterday."

Then they were all climbing into a car in the darkness.

"Mama! Is Mama here?" Elena had asked, stumbling into the back seat as the car's motor was shifted into motion. Soon she felt her mother's arms encircling her.

After that, as they were whisked away through the Cuban countryside, Mama told them about her own escape. She had walked out the back gate and down the alley to the bridge, just as if she were on her way to the store. She had not stopped there, but had crossed the river to the house of a friend—the very friend who was now taking them away in his car. Since the Santeros had all left the house one by one, no one would suspect anything.

"Where are we going, Papa?" Benito asked, when there was a lull.

"To la Isabel," Papa told him, quietly.

Benito could not see a thing because it was a very dark night, but he could remember. He thought back to the trip he had taken with Michael to visit Doña Miranda at la Isabel.

He remembered how blue the sky had been that day. There were cane fields fanning out in every direction from the railroad with clusters of palm trees growing here and there. In the distance, now and then, they could see the white roof of a sugar mill.

Benito also remembered la Isabel as it had looked that day—the palms on the town square braced against the brisk breeze coming in from the sea, the white gulls circling and crying overhead.

He lifted his head and sniffed. Yes, there it was, that same brisk breeze, strong with the familiar odor of fish yet somehow alive and vital. They were in la Isabel.

A few minutes later, they were out of the car and stumbling across the wooden boardwalk that led to Doña Miranda's house. Benito could hear the sleepy slurp-slurp-slurp of waves washing against the piles under their feet. He could feel the warm lump that was Blanco, inside his jacket.

"*¡Viva la Cuba!*" he said under his breath as he stepped into a little rowboat, moored alongside.

"*Dios mediante,*" Papa whispered back. Benito could tell that he was not saying the words lightly. Papa spoke the words as a prayer.

Then Papa helped the others in—Elena and Mama with Carmen in her arms. Someone took up the oars and the little boat shoved off into the darkness.

A Chance for Happiness

Afterwards, that night and the next day always seemed like a nightmare to Benito. It was as if those hours had been cut loose from the ones before and after, to drift, surrounded by a vast grey sky and wind-tumbled waves, in his mind forever.

At first, their bodies were stiff with fear of the patrol boats along the shores of Cuba—boats whose one purpose was to prevent the enemies of the Revolution from escaping. But at last there came the transfer from the small rowboat to a much bigger one. Even in the dark, Benito knew there were other people on it, but he could not tell who. The motor revved into a roar and knifed the water into a spray that wet their faces and clothing—a spray of hope in the covering darkness.

The big motor boat ate up the miles and after hours of travel, they finally tumbled ashore on the barren rocks of Cay Sal Bank. They were thirty miles from Cuba and fifty miles from Key West, Florida. Their bodies shivering with anxiety, they waited for rescue, watching the sun come up.

"But suppose no one ever finds us?" Elena asked. Benito noticed that the little crease, a sure sign that she was afraid of something, was on her forehead all the time, now.

Papa put her arm around her. "Every day, a coast guard plane from the United States goes over these rocks. If the pilot sees anyone he sends help. So all we need to do is wait and someone will find us. *¡Dios mediante!*"

Even the waiting seemed like a nightmare to Benito. But the coming of the plane and the trip in the coast guard cutter that took them to Miami was not a nightmare but a dream. Once there, Papa was whisked away to be questioned while the rest of the family waited at the Refugee Center.

Elena watched him go, her eyes wide with fear. Then she burst into noisy tears. Mama and Benito looked at each other, over her head. Elena *never* cried!

"It is because Papa does not have the right papers for us to enter," Mama explained. "Don't cry, Elena. As soon as they are sure that Papa is not a spy, they will let him come back to us."

In spite of everything that Benito and Mama could say, Elena kept right on sobbing. Carmen, who was used to being the center of attention, was not happy about this sudden change. She put back her head and howled, too.

Suddenly, a big bronzed hand came down and clapped itself over Carmen's mouth. In her surprise, she stopped her screaming.

"Carlos!" Mama said.

Tío Carlos was a big man. He had a shaggy look about him, but his eyes twinkled a welcome to them all.

"He looks like a big dog," Benito thought. "A nice, shaggy dog that you could trust anywhere."

"Josefa!" Tío Carlos said, as he swept Mama into his arms.

"Oh, Carlos, it is good to see you," Mama said. Then she put her head down on his shoulder and began to cry, too. "We had to go for Papa's sake. We . . ."

"There, there!" Tío Carlos said. "You are here now, safe and sound. Soon, Papa will be released and you will all be able to start life over again."

He looked over her shoulder at Benito, Elena, and Carmen, who were all standing there, wide-eyed.

"It looks as if tears were plentiful," he said, with a smile. "We'll have to watch ourselves, Benito, or we'll be afloat in a minute."

Carmen and Elena had never met Tío Carlos, and Benito could hardly remember him. Yet within ten minutes they felt like old friends. Tío Carlos knew exactly what to do, too, because he had already helped other Cuban relatives who were refugees.

"Now, before we leave, I will just check at the Church World Service office," he said. "Why don't you and the girls wait here, Josefa? Benito, would you like to come with me?"

"What is Church World Service?" Benito asked as he tagged after his uncle.

"That is quite a question, Ben. It is—well, how shall I say it? An organization to help people all over the world who are homeless to find homes. It helps people in other ways, too."

"But who is it that does these things?" Benito was still puzzled.

"Christians in the evangelical churches give money," Tío Carlos said. "In many different congregations, offerings are taken for this. They know that the churches here in Miami cannot do everything that needs to be done for all of us—the need is too big. But here we are." Tío Carlos smiled as he stepped to the information desk of Church World Service. "I must postpone the rest of my lecture on Church World Service till some other time."

Benito did not listen to what Tío Carlos was saying to the man at the desk, at first. He was thinking about what he had heard. Had some boy, just about his own age, given money to help them? Suddenly, he heard Papa's name.

"They should wait to register here until Dr. Santero himself can come," the man explained. He spoke in Spanish as if it were his own language. It seemed that everyone here in Miami spoke Spanish.

"Yes," Tío Carlos said. "In a few days, I will bring them, Señor Smith."

"You realize that the only solution is resettlement somewhere else, don't you, Señor Gonzalez?" Mr. Smith went on, earnestly.

Tío Carlos looked troubled. "Resettlement is a hard word, Señor Smith. It means going where they do not know anyone. I will not talk of that to Josefa just yet. She is my sister and has suffered many things. And she is welcome in my home for as long as she wishes to stay."

"Don't they have any friends elsewhere in the United States?" Mr. Smith asked.

"I do not think so," Tío Carlos began, but Benito tugged at his sleeve.

"There is the Reed family, Tío Carlos. Michael is a

good friend of mine. They were neighbors of ours in Sagua."

Mr. Smith turned to Benito. "Reed, you say. Why, we're corresponding with them right now. He and I were co-workers in Cuba and they have been very anxious about some of their friends there."

"They lived on the corner of our block," Benito said.

He closed his eyes for a moment. Suddenly, he was back in Cuba, standing there in the bright sunshine. Michael stood beside him. Together, they were watching their butterfly kite fluttering in the sky, tugging at the string that held it.

"Perhaps they would be willing to help now," Mr. Smith said, thoughtfully, and Benito came back to the present with a jolt.

"Let us say nothing about all this to Mama just yet," Tío Carlos said as he and Benito went back to join the rest.

"About resettlement?"

"About that or the Reeds. They may not be able to help even if they would like to do so. And there is no use in raising hopes that come to nothing in the end. Mama has suffered enough."

Benito drew himself up tall. "Of course, I will not mention it, Tío Carlos. You can depend on me."

During the days that followed, while they settled down in Miami, the word *resettlement* was not mentioned at all. Yet that strange, cold word seemed to fill the sky for Benito.

Mr. Smith had said that resettlement was the only way; Benito could see why, even for himself. Tío Carlos was sheltering his wife's sister and her two little girls, plus the Santero family. He had three children of his own. Sometimes it seemed as if the little six-room house would burst at the seams!

Yet, to think of leaving Miami was almost like leaving Cuba all over again. Here, everyone seemed to speak Spanish. There was bright sunshine and tall palms and wide blue skies; the stores sold *yuca* and *plátanos* just as they did in Cuba.

As soon as Papa was released, he began to look for work. Day after day he tramped the streets, but each evening he came home with a discouraged droop to his shoulders. When he finally did find something to do, it was only washing dishes in a café. Papa, who was used to performing operations with delicate instruments! Benito could hardly bear to look at his father's water-soaked hands after a day of washing dishes.

"It is better than being idle," Papa said cheerfully. He was not working that day, so he and Benito walked blocks until they finally came to a wide, empty beach. It brought them memories of Cuba.

They stood for a while in silence, watching the waves follow each other up to the white sand, each one a little higher than the last. Benito felt sure that Papa had something he wanted to say to him; the word *resettlement* hung like a black cloud in the air between them.

"Has Tío Carlos said anything to you about our going elsewhere?" Papa asked finally.

Benito nodded his head. He could not seem to speak. "Perhaps we will go back—" he began.

Papa's face creased into a frown. "I have seen those who come here to Miami and wait, day after day, for something to happen. They look back. They hope. They pray. After a while, it almost seems that they believe that a fairy godmother will wave a wand and help them, or that there is some magic in the intensity of their desires."

Benito did not say anything. He knew that Papa had forgotten whom he was talking to. He was saying the kind of thing he would say to Tío Carlos. If Benito kept quiet, he might go on.

"We cannot live in the past, my son," Papa said, after a minute of silence. "These people who try to do so are sad—very sad. We must look at the way things are now, no matter how hard it seems."

"So we should forget Cuba. . . " Benito was not really taking to Papa; he was thinking aloud.

"Never!" Papa shouted. Then he caught himself. "I am sorry. I did not mean to shout at you, Benito. We *cannot* forget the past. It will go with us, whether we like it or not. Sometimes, it will bring us much pain, but there will be times when it brings us much happiness, too."

"What do you mean?"

Papa stopped to think for a minute. Then he said, "Well, it is a little like having Blanco with you. He is something out of the past; sometimes he reminds you of Sagua so much that you have pain. Yet, you would not want to lose him, would you?"

"No!" This time it was Benito who shouted. Then he knelt down in the sand and with his finger drew a rough map of Cuba. "I think I see what you mean," he said.

After a bit, he went on. He tried to sound as grown-up as possible as he said, "But there is all this talk about another war, Papa. Suppose. . ."

Papa shook his head sadly. "Suppose, yes. That is all we Cubans who love democracy are doing—*supposing*. We already know that war is not really the answer. No. What we must do is keep the past while we make the most of the present."

In the stillness that followed, Benito thought of many things that he could not put into words. He thought about other differences—the church, for instance. In Cuba, Papa had seldom gone; here, they all went to the Evangelical church with Tío Carlos. It was a different kind of service, yet the same in some ways. They did not need to forget the past or renounce it. Sometimes it would bring comfort and sometimes pain. But now, they must live in the present.

"The present," he said softly.

"It must be." Papa looked far out across the sea, to the far place where it merged with the sky. "It is not easy for me, either."

Benito looked at him. Always, Papa had seemed so strong, so sure of himself; but he loved Cuba, too. He loved being a doctor and helping sick people. Now, it was all gone. He was washing dishes in a café.

Then Papa looked up and went on. "But there are Mama and the girls, Benito. *We men*—we must be strong for them."

Benito almost felt that in one minute he had grown several inches taller. *We men,* Papa had said!

"Besides, the present will not stay empty, Benito. We will find a place, *Dios mediante,* where I can practice medicine, and where we can settle down and make a new

life for ourselves," Papa said it reverently, like a prayer.

During the days that followed, Benito straightened his shoulders whenever he thought of that talk with Papa. He began to help Mama more, too. *We men,* Papa had said.

One day, the doorbell rang. "I'll get it," Benito called from the kitchen where he was putting away groceries.

When he opened the door, he could only stand and stare.

"Señor Reed!" he gasped finally.

And who was that with him? A tall, thin boy—taller than Benito remembered but with the same straw colored hair, the same sprinkle of freckles on his nose, the same wide grin.

"Michael!" Benito said at the very same minute that Michael gasped, "Benito!" And the next minute they were shaking hands, and greeting each other over and over—in Spanish and English.

Later, when Mama was talking to Mr. Reed, he and Michael stared at each other. Benito felt as if they were strangers—as if this were another boy, wearing Michael's freckles.

"Did you ever finish the butterfly kite?" Michael asked suddenly.

Benito remembered the fun of fitting fragile bits of

colored paper into place. Suddenly, Michael looked familiar after all.

"No—I never did," he said. "It was no fun alone."

"Never mind—we'll build a bigger one and fly it together, this time."

"How—how do you mean?" Benito asked.

"Maybe I shouldn't say it yet but Dad'll get around to it after a while anyway." Michael leaned his mouth close to Benito's ear. "We've found a good job for your father, with my uncle. Helping in a clinic—even though your father can't practice medicine until he gets a license. There's a house for you folks, too, right near us."

For a minute Benito felt dizzy. Things were moving too fast for him. He felt Michael's hand on his shoulder.

"This time, it's my turn," Michael said. "I will show you my country, just as you showed me yours. It is not little and full of sunshine, like Cuba, but it is big and brave and exciting."

Blanco came and wrapped himself around Benito's ankle. When Benito picked him up, he purred loudly.

"That's good, Michael," Benito said. He really meant it, too. He and Michael could share the past, but they could also go out and face the present. Now, with his friend's hand on his shoulder, life no longer seemed empty and hard, but warm with a chance for happiness.

2 Casa Rivera

¡ENTRE!

"¡Entre!" says Juan of Puerto Rico. Juan will tell you about how lost he felt when Papa went to Chicago and disappeared. In Chicago, Papa thought there would be work to do and that he could support his family there. Life would be better, he thought, and he would not need to get crippled and bent, trying to make a living from the little fields of his Puerto Rican hill farm.

Since Puerto Rico is not a foreign country, like Cuba and Mexico, no one needs to wait for emigration papers to come to the United States. So thousands of Puerto Ricans do come each year to try to find a better way of life. Often the father of the family comes first. He may work here for six months or a year, until he has enough money to send for other members of the family.

There are many adjustments that Puerto Ricans must make when they come to the United States. They often live under unbelievably crowded conditions; their language and customs set them apart. But churches throughout the country are helping in many ways. In Chicago, for example, the churches have created Casa Central to help families like Juan's to get settled.

Casa Central is a co-operative organization that is sponsored by churches in Chicago to help Spanish speaking families. Helpers at Casa Central hold vacation church schools and fresh air programs like Friendly Town, through which Spanish speaking children can visit farms in the area. Casa Central also provides clinics and adult education programs—the things that would be too expensive for any one church to carry out alone.

The Empty Mailbox

Juan Rivera was perched on a window sill in the living room. By leaning back a little, he could see down the steep Puerto Rican hillside to the patch of banana trees, the little white church, and the winding road beyond. A few chickens scratched in the dooryard and around the front steps. His sisters and brother—Alicia, Candita, and Julio—were playing around the doorstep, outside.

"But this is our home!" Mama was saying. "Now Papa is gone—who knows what has happened to him? We must stay here and wait for him!"

Juan jerked his head inside and looked around the room. It was crowded with relatives. Uncle Jorge sat across from Juan. He was chewing one end of his mustache—a sure sign that he was worried. Uncle Tomás looked sharply at Mama. Juan knew he was not pleased at the way she was speaking up.

"It is not a woman's place to rule the family," Tío Tomás said, heavily.

"I must do what my husband would wish," Mama said. Her voice was lower, more respectful now.

Juan looked at Mama with a new respect. Mama was a big woman; so big that their flimsy little house shook when she walked across the floor. In spite of this, Papa had always looked out for her. Papa and Grandfather always decided about things. Even when they asked Mama, she usually said, "Oh, I don't know." Yet now, when the men of the family were saying that Papa meant to go away and leave them in Puerto Rico, she spoke up splendidly.

Juan turned to look at Grandfather, too. He sat in the best chair, just inside the door. His hands were clasped over the chair arms. They were withered, like the claws of a bird. Grandfather's back was bent from years of working in the fields of his little hill farm.

"That is why Papa left Puerto Rico," Juan thought. "He wanted a better future for Julio and me. No matter what they say, he did not go because he wanted to get rid of us. I will not believe that!"

Grandfather lifted his head. A silence fell on them all. "You say you have heard from him only once since he left, María?" he asked.

"Only once, Grandfather," Mama told him. "That was right after he arrived in Chicago. Since then—nothing!"

Juan had a queer, hollow feeling at the pit of his stomach. He remembered those days of waiting. Each day Mama said, "Surely we will hear today!" Then, as the days passed, she did not mention it any more. Juan began to hate those half-mile hikes out to their mailbox, because each time he came home empty handed.

"All the same, I will not believe that Papa meant to go away and forget all about us. Something terrible has happened to him. I know it!" Mama spoke firmly.

"It is not a woman's place . . ." Tío Tomás began again.

"I don't understand what's happened to you, María," Grandfather said mildly. "We have gathered here to help you, yet you keep treating us as if we were enemies."

"I am sorry, Grandfather," Mama said. "I will listen to what you have to say—but not if you talk against Cristino. He is my husband. He is good. I do not believe that he went away and forgot all about us."

"Well, it is right that a woman should stand by her husband," Tío Tomás conceded. He was always talking about *right* and *wrong*. "But you must listen to reason too, María. We must decide what you and the children should do."

"Why can't we go to Chicago and join Papa?" Juan hadn't meant to say that aloud. The words were spoken before he could stop himself. He shuddered at what Tío Tomás might say!

Immediately, a babble of talk broke out. To Juan's surprise, no one scolded him for talking out of turn. It almost seemed as if he had said something they were all thinking about.

The talk went on and on. Tío Carlos spoke strongly against their going.

"Where would the money come from?" he asked.

Juan knew why he brought that up. Tío Carlos had a grocery store, down at the foot of the mountain where they lived. Of all the family, he was the one who had the most ready money.

"But they must do *something*," Tío Tomás argued. "Whatever they do will cost money. If they could join Cristino. . ."

"That was what Cristino always planned," Aunt Sofía spoke up for the first time.

"But suppose he really has deserted—" Tío Jorge looked at Mama and went on hastily. "Or suppose something terrible has happened to him. Then we'd need to bring them all back to Puerto Rico again."

Mama sat up straight. Juan knew that she was going

to take Papa's part again. All during these hours when the rest had been saying that Papa meant to go away and forget his family, Mama had refused to believe them.

"One little moment, please," Grandfather said. He straightened himself in his chair, while everyone turned to listen. Grandfather never raised his voice, but the minute he spoke, the rest paid attention.

"María, you *must* think about this whether you want to or not," Grandfather said. "Suppose we do send you and the children to Chicago. What will you do if you cannot find Cristino?"

They all turned to look at Mama. From where he was sitting, Juan could see the little hollow at her throat. The pulse beat swiftly up and down in it. After a little, he could not bear to look any longer. Suddenly, he remembered something.

"Tío Alfredo lives in Chicago," Juan said. "I have his address—he sent me a letter last Christmas."

Relief spread across all the faces, as if the sun had suddenly come right into their shabby *casita*.

"He is Juan's godfather—of course!" Tío Tomás exclaimed. "I had forgotten."

"*¡Bueno, bueno!*" Tío Carlos added. "Alfredo will help you, if you cannot find Cristino."

"With Alfredo there, I can send you to Chicago in

peace." Grandfather was nodding and smiling too. "Now we must make plans for your going."

Juan did not know whether he was glad or not about the turn plans had taken. Chicago was so far away! But Papa was there!

"Juan! Why don't you go look for the mail?" Mama said.

It was hard to leave just then, but Juan knew Mama wanted to know whether Papa had written. At one time, the mail was not important, but now, every day brought the Rivera family hope that they might have a message from Papa.

Of course, Papa himself could not write. He had never been to school. The one note they had received from him had been only a few words, scribbled on the back of a green sheet with an advertisement for fur coats on the other side. The person who wrote it for Papa could not spell very well. Yet, Mama kept it carefully, because it made Papa seem closer to them.

As Juan walked down the steps, Candita stood up. "Where are you going, Juan? Take me, too! ¡*Por favor!*" she asked, running across the room.

Juan hesitated. He had important things to think about; he didn't want the others tagging along. And if Candita went, they'd have to come, too.

Candita wrapped her arms around his legs. "I want to go! I want to go!" she said. "I can ride Treeta Valeeta."

"*Ay de mí*," Juan groaned.

Treeta Valeeta was Candita's imaginary pony. No one knew where the funny name came from—probably out of Candita's own head. She had been sick so much when she was a baby. Perhaps that was why she played so many pretend games. Now, she mounted her imaginary horse, put her feet into the stirrups, picked up the reins, and was ready to go.

Alicia came dashing up. "Let me go, too! Let me go, too!"

Julio raced after her. "Me, too! Me, too!" he screamed. Then he added, "Where are you going, Juan?"

"*Ay de mí*," Juan muttered again. "Those youngsters! They don't care where they go, just so they can be going!"

"I'm going for the mail," Juan said.

He looked around the circle of faces. Sturdy Julio, aged seven. Six-year-old Alicia with her tangled curls. Candita, a four-year-old with merry eyes peeping from her dark little face—so dark that they sometimes called her *Negrita*. They all waited to hear what Juan would say.

"Okay, you can all come!" Juan said. Then, as they raced ahead with Candita riding Treeta Valeeta, he put his head inside the door. "I'm taking the little ones with me, Mama."

They took a path down the steep hillside until it dipped into the creek bottom. Mama did her laundry here. Candita rode Treeta Valeeta onto a big flat rock where Mama always scrubbed the overalls and dresses, after soaking them in the water for a while. The path skirted the bushes that were Mama's clothesline.

They climbed the next hillock, where the church stood. Juan looked around eagerly. Sometimes the pastor, Brother Mercado, came there to study on Saturday. Yes, there he was—standing at the church door, looking out.

"*Buenas días,* Brother Mercado," Juan said. He stepped closer to shake hands. "Come! Don't forget your manners, Julio, Alicia, Candita!" They all came running to say *buenas días* and shake hands, too.

"Any news from your father, Juan?" Brother Mercado asked.

"Not yet. Not since that first letter. We're on the way to the mailbox now." Juan dragged one foot back and forth through the grass beside the church door. "Grandfather and the others are talking about sending us to Chicago."

"Really? And what happens if you cannot find him?"

Juan could not understand why Brother Mercado

looked so disturbed. "Uncle Alfredo, my godfather, lives in Chicago. If we can't find Papa, we'll ask him to help us."

"What is Chicago?" Candita demanded suddenly. She was letting Treeta Valeeta graze beside the church.

"It's a big city," Juan explained. "A big friendly city, with high buildings—like San Juan."

He thought of Chicago like that, ever since the day the Rivera family went all the way to San Juan to see Papa off on the plane. There had been tall buildings, but the sun shone down on them. And the *avenidas* were lined with palm trees. Chicago was surely as friendly as San Juan.

Brother Mercado cleared his throat. "I went to school in the United States—the church there made it possible for me to go," he said. "And I'm afraid Chicago is not nearly as much like San Juan as you think, Juan. It is much bigger and less friendly."

He looked from Candita's face to Julio's and Alicia's. They were all watching him with unwinking stares. How could he ever tell them—how it had been with him, in Chicago?

"Why don't the three of you go on down to the mailbox?" Juan said quickly. "I'll talk to Brother Mercado until you come back."

They went, although Julio dragged his feet and kept

looking back. He knew Juan and Brother Mercado wanted to talk about something they did not want them to hear.

"Now—tell me. What is Chicago *really* like?" Juan demanded.

Brother Mercado sighed. "It is a big place—you can't know how big until you see it. Crowds of people go up and down the sidewalks, without paying attention to anyone else. It can be lonely, very lonely—especially if you know no one."

"You think we shouldn't go?"

"I'm not saying that. But it's not as simple as you think. I will feel better about your going if you have the address of Casa Central—a place where you can get help if you need it. The churches of Chicago established it to help Puerto Rican families get settled, get medical help, learn English, and the like."

"Casa Central," Juan repeated, half to himself. "For Puerto Rican families." He felt that Chicago would surely have many friendly people in its churches if they were so kind to strangers from faraway Puerto Rico.

"Here, I will write the name and address on a slip of paper for you," Brother Mercado was saying. "If you really need help, go there. And one more thing, Juan."

"Yes, Brother Mercado?"

"You must remember that things are different in Chicago. Some people there look down on Puerto Ricans—just because—well—they are Puerto Ricans."

Juan stared at Brother Mercado. "What do you mean?"

"It's hard to explain. Here in Puerto Rico, we think of people as people. If they are old, we respect them."

Juan thought of Grandfather. "Yes," he agreed.

"Rich or poor, we respect them for what they are, for what they can do."

"Yes," Juan agreed, again. He was thinking of Uncle Carlos and his grocery store.

"This isn't true everywhere. Sometimes—" Brother Mercado hesitated. "Sometimes people there even look down on others because the color of their faces is dark."

"What do you mean?" Juan leaned closer to Brother Mercado. He could hear the children's voices on the trail just below. In a minute, they would be back.

"I don't understand either," Brother Mercado said. "I found it so and I felt I must warn you. Your little sister Candita is very dark—"

"Candita! But she is the sweetest and brightest of us all!"

"There are people who will see that and there are some who won't. Some will look only at her skin color.

That is all that matters. If it is dark, then that is *malo, muy malo,* very bad."

"And they look down on you for something you cannot help?" Juan simply couldn't believe that.

"Sh! Here comes Candita now!" Brother Mercado put his finger to his lips.

They both watched Candita ride Treeta Valeeta up the trail. Her eyes were snapping as she jogged along on her imaginary pony. When she came to the church, she called, "*Jo,* whoa!" and jumping off, threw the reins over a fence post.

Juan looked at Brother Mercado and shook his head. "I don't understand," he said. "I don't understand at all!"

"Well, let us see," Brother Mercado said, kindly. "There may be a letter from your papa today."

But when Julio and Alicia came running up the trail they were empty handed.

"Thank you, Brother Mercado," said Juan, shaking his hand and then turning slowly in the direction of their *casita.* "We must go and tell Mama and the others right away. This means we will be going to Chicago."

A Strange City

When Juan and the little ones got home, Tío Tomás was almost ready to leave. When he found out that Papa had not written, he drew Juan to one side.

"We have made arrangements for your family to go to Chicago," he said. "You must remember, Juan, that you will be the head of the family until you find Papa. Chicago will be new and strange. And Mama is a woman. She is not used to deciding things."

Juan swallowed hard. "But—but I'm only twelve, Tío Tomás!"

"I know. You are too young, perhaps. But you speak English, which Mama does not. And you are a man. One cannot expect a woman to be the head of the family—at least, not a woman like Mama, who has always had a husband or a father to decide things for her. I see no other way, Juan."

"Well, I will do my best, Tío Tomás," Juan said.

During the days that followed, Juan was too busy and too excited to think much about being the head of the family. He even forgot what Brother Mercado had told him. Not until after the plane trip to Chicago did he think of it again. He and his family were in a taxi, weaving in and out of traffic, up one street and down another in a confusing way. People walked much faster in Chicago than in Puerto Rico and jostled each other on the sidewalks.

"Brother Mercado was certainly right—this city isn't a bit like San Juan," he muttered to himself.

"You gave the driver Papa's address?" Mama said to Juan, for the the third time. Mama's round face had lost its usual cheerful look.

"Yes, Mama. Of course."

She leaned back with a sigh. "I did not think it would be this far. But then, I did not know that Chicago was so big. My feet hurt after that walk at the airport."

The taxi pulled over to the curb. "Here we are, lady," the driver said.

Mama and the others stood on the sidewalk, looking tired and lost. Juan paid the driver and then turned toward them.

For a minute, he felt as lost and lonely as he had ever

felt in his life. He did not know, any more than Mama, which apartment was Papa's in this tall building. He hated to step inside that strange door—and what would they do if Papa wasn't there? Then he remembered that he was the head of the family.

"Come, Mama," he said aloud. He felt tall and old—almost as old as Grandfather! "We will ask about Papa on the first floor here."

They stepped inside, into a little square entrance hall. Juan glanced up the steep stairway, then knocked on the door to his left. From beyond it, he could hear radio music. A minute later, it opened just a crack.

"Yes?" said a voice.

"Does Cristino Rivera live here?" Juan asked.

Instantly, the door opened and an enormous man stepped out. "My friend, Cristino? Well, he was here, but he left. You will know where to find him, no?"

Juan shook his head, biting his lips. "The only letter we had from Papa after he left Puerto Rico had this address."

The man's face changed. Its oily friendliness dissolved into a scowl.

"So. He didn't let you know where he went? Well, he spent only a month in this building. Then he left."

In a moment, the Riveras were back on the sidewalk,

standing in a little huddle. The big man followed them. His mouth settled into grim lines.

"He left without paying his rent, too. From now on, I collect beforehand, see?"

The big man stepped over to the curb. "Puerto Ricans!" he muttered savagely, spitting into the gutter.

"Juan, what *will* we do now?" Mama's voice trembled a little again. When it came to defending Papa, Mama knew what to do. But here, on the streets of Chicago, she was helpless.

"We'll go to Tío Alfredo," Juan said.

There was another trip in a taxi. This driver leaned on his horn and darted in and out among cars and buses in a hair-raising way. Before long, he pulled up in front of a tall building, set in a wide lawn. The building had wings jutting out at strange angles and tier after tier of porches.

"Tío Alfredo lives here? He must be very rich," Mama said.

"You're sure this is the right place?" Juan asked the driver.

"Dead sure," the driver said. His smile was friendly. "This is a new project—opened just about a year ago. If you'll check the mailboxes on first floor, you'll find your uncle's name."

The next half hour was a nightmare for them all. They were afraid to try the self-service elevator, so they climbed up stairway after stairway. Even after they found the right floor, it was not easy to find Apartment 610. They had to go down one of the long open porches they had seen from below.

Juan knocked at the door and waited. Mama and the younger children huddled around him.

A long time later, as Juan was ready to knock again, the door opened a crack.

"Good day, Tío Alfredo," Juan said uncertainly. It was hard to be sure whose eyes were staring at him when that was all he could see!

Whoever was on the other side of the door seemed confused, too.

"Who is speaking, please?" a voice asked.

"I'm Juan Rivera," Juan said. "I am looking for my godfather, Alfredo Melendez. Mama and the little ones are here with me. We just came from Puerto Rico."

The door swung open slowly. The face that looked at them was not Tío Alfredo's face, although the boy had Alfredo's nose and straight jaw.

"I'm Manuel Melendez. Papa is sleeping," he explained. "He works nights, you know. But *entre!*—Mama will know whether we should wake him or not."

They went into a crowded little kitchen. Juan could not remember Aunt Rosita at all. It was so long since she and Tío Alfredo had left Puerto Rico.

"So you are Alfredo's little godson," she said as she bustled around, filling a coffee pot and putting it on the stove. "I suppose Cristino is with you, María? Surely you did not come alone?"

Mama looked down at her hands, clasped tightly in her lap to keep them from trembling. Juan saw that she could not speak, so he answered for her.

"Papa is here in Chicago already," he explained.

Tía Rosita held the coffee pot suspended over a cup. A thin stream of very black coffee fell into the cup.

"I have made this the Puerto Rican way. People here —what they make should not be called coffee! In all my eight years here, I've never learned to like it."

She handed round the cups and then, taking her own, sat down. The kitchen stool creaked as she eased herself onto it.

"You have Cristino's address then, María?" she asked.

Juan wished she wouldn't keep pestering Mama with questions like that. He was just a boy, but he was head of the family now. Once more, he answered for her.

"We went to the address Papa gave us, but he moved some time ago. The landlord does not know where."

"What is it, Rosita? We have company, no?" Tío Alfredo was in his pajamas and his hair was uncombed.

Alfredo's lips fell into a straight line as he shook hands with each one of the Rivera's and gave his godson, Juan, an extra pat on the back. Then he accepted some coffee and sat down, draping his bare feet over the chair rungs. All eyes were on him as he slowly stirred his coffee— round and round.

"They are looking for Cristino," Tía Rosita explained. Her look at Alfredo over the coffee cup was long and hard. Seeing it, Juan felt a queer empty feeling inside.

"You will help us, Alfredo," Mama said. She set down her coffee cup on one corner of the table. "Chicago is a much bigger place than I knew."

Tío Alfredo shook his head sadly. "I don't know, María. It is, as you say, a big place. And Cristino is only one small person in it."

"But what shall we do?" Mama's voice sounded sharp because she was so worried. "Oh, Alfredo—"

In a minute, she would be asking Tío Alfredo to take them in. And Juan knew he would never do that—not with Tía Rosita's hard eyes on him.

"Things are different, here," Juan thought to himself.

Tío Alfredo moved uneasily. He looked to Juan for support. "I am only one person, María. You must not expect miracles from me. Cristino could drift around Chicago for months without seeing us."

Juan closed his eyes for just one minute. Instantly, he was back on the sunny hillside in Puerto Rico. Brother Mercado was writing a name and address on a slip of paper.

"You can get help from a place called Casa Central," Brother Mercado had said.

"Do you know about Casa Central, Tío Alfredo?" Juan asked.

The whole room seemed to lighten as he spoke. He could tell by the pleased look on Tía Rosita's face that she was happy at this suggestion. Tío Alfredo beamed round on them all.

"Of course. They have helped many of our friends. How could I have forgotten? At Casa Central they will help you."

Tía Rosita hurried to look up the address in the phone book and Tío Alfredo went off to get dressed. Then he called a cab and escorted them downstairs and out to the curb.

"These projects—they are wonderful things," he said, looking up at the big building. "Before, we lived in a third floor walk-up apartment with no heat. And rats all over the place. Here, we are comfortable. We had to wait our turn, of course. And just to think that they pulled down many old apartments so that this one could be built here."

Tío Alfredo was all smiles now, pumping the hands of all the Riveras as he wished them luck and all but lifted them into the taxi. They were being whisked away before Mama had a chance to speak.

"But, Juan—I thought he would ask us to stay," she said. "After all, he *is* your godfather."

"It's different here, Mama," Juan began slowly. "Tío Alfredo has been here a long time. He has forgotten the old ways."

Juan went on, trying to smooth things over. He knew Tío Alfredo had talked fast to cover up his embarrassment at not doing all that a godfather was expected to do. He had slipped a five dollar bill into Juan's hand as they left. It crackled against his palm as he folded it into a tight little square.

"I am afraid here, Juan," Mama whispered. "Chicago is so big and so different—"

"But *Papa* is here," Juan said. He cupped Mama's hand in both of his. "When we find Papa, we will be all right."

"Dios mediante," whispered Mama.

"When we find Papa—" Juan thought of those words

often in the days and weeks that followed. And during those days they learned that everything depended on Casa Central.

"Why, it's a church!" Mama had said, when she got out of the taxi and first saw the building.

But after they were inside they soon learned that it wasn't used as a church anymore—only a place where the church did some of its work of helping others, a woman explained. Then she asked them many questions. Juan did not have to answer for Mama, because this woman could speak Spanish. Everyone at Casa Central spoke Spanish, it seemed.

And everyone was kind. No one hurried the Riveras out into the street with smooth words. The helpers all knew how it felt to be a stranger in a big city like Chicago. They provided an apartment and money for food. They gave the Riveras hope about Papa. They explained that many other Puerto Rican families had been separated for a time and later reunited.

"Sooner or later, he'll come here," the woman who registered them said, with a smile. "At least it sometimes seems as if every Puerto Rican in Chicago does. And if a Cristino Rivera comes, we'll send him to you. Why, you may hear a knock on your door at any time and open it to find your Papa there."

"Dios mediante," Mama said under her breath. "If God wills it."

But the days passed and Papa did not come. One day, Candita began to look pale and droopy. She stabled Treeta Valeeta in one corner of the kitchen and left her there. She did not go outside to play.

Mama fussed and worried. She finally had Juan take Candita to the Casa Central clinic. Dr. Martinez shook his head when he examined her.

"This little one needs sun and good food and air," he said.

For the first time in many weeks Juan felt that he could not swallow the lump in his throat. He had tried to take Papa's place but if Candita got sick and. . . This was too much for him.

"But, doctor, we *cannot,*" he said between stiff lips. *"¡ Es imposible!"*

"Relax, son," the doctor said. "She needs to go but we will not expect *you* to send her. Do you know about Friendly Town?"

Juan wondered if he looked as bewildered as he felt. "I once thought Chicago was a friendly city, like San Juan," he said. "But Friendly Town—of that I have not heard."

"Candita will be better when she gets some fresh air

and sunshine." Dr. Martinez smiled as he picked up a pencil and began filling out a printed slip of paper. "Tell your mother to come to see me next week. I think we may have good news for her."

Then Dr. Martinez leaned back in his chair and looked at Juan. There were others waiting, but he sounded as if he had all day to talk when he said, "You've had a rough time of it, haven't you?"

Something hard inside Juan, something kept tight like the string on a violin, suddenly snapped. With Tío Alfredo, he had expected kindness and had not received it. He could be bold and brave then. But now . . . he laid his face on his arms for a minute.

"You are very kind, Dr. Martinez," he said in a choked voice.

Then he sat up and began to tell the doctor all about everything—especially about Papa.

Welcome Home!

The words came tumbling out so fast his tongue almost tripped over them, as Juan told Dr. Martinez about his troubles. Dr. Martinez listened as intently as if he had never heard the sad story before—even though he had heard hundreds of sad stories from other Puerto Ricans. When Juan had finished, they sat in silence for a minute.

"I can't go out and find your father, Juan," the doctor said. "As your godfather said—Chicago is a big place. Someday he may come to Casa Central for help. We will all keep our eyes open here."

"But why didn't Uncle Alfredo want to help us?" Juan asked, in a small voice. "Are things so different here in Chicago?"

Dr. Martinez pulled his chin. "I am not sure how to say this, Juan. But—well, in Puerto Rico families stick together. You know that when you talk about your family, you mean uncles, aunts, grandparents, godparents, and so on. But here, when we talk about a family, we mean only the father, mother, and children—that's all. Yes, let's face it! We Puerto Ricans are Americans. But— it *is* different here."

Juan's eyes grew big. "But who helps when things go wrong? Who looks after the children when the parents cannot?"

Dr. Martinez pulled his chin, thoughtfully. "Well, welfare agencies take care of many of them."

Juan still looked blank. The doctor tried again, "Welfare agencies are—well, look! Casa Central is one. It costs Uncle Alfredo and his family a lot to live. If he took you in, one family would have to bear the burden alone. If we help you here at Casa Central, many people share that burden—the people who gave money to Casa Central, the people who work here, and the Christians in the churches here in Chicago that co-operate with us. This way, many together do the helping."

"Is this a better way?" Juan asked.

Dr. Martinez put his arm around Juan's shoulders. "I didn't say that. It's good to be part of a family—good to feel responsible for others, just as they are responsible for you. But, when this no longer happens, then another good way is for Christians to help each other. Also, their helping can include those who have no families. *¿Entiende,* do you understand?"

Juan nodded his head. "I think so. It is good for us Puerto Ricans to be concerned for those who are not in our own *familias.*"

After a minute of silence, Juan went on. "But—but the people here in Chicago do not like us." He made a flat statement, not a question. He was remembering the way the big man who had been Papa's landlord said, "Puerto Ricans!" then leaned over to spit into the gutter.

"That is different from Puerto Rico, too." The doctor spoke sadly. He was not smiling now. "There, it does not matter that a man's face is dark."

"I can't understand it," Juan said. "The color of your face is something you can't help or change. Candita is dark, that is true. But she is the sweetest of us all."

"This is a lesson we need to learn," Dr. Martinez said heavily. "Perhaps we who have come from Puerto Rico can help others learn it."

"Muchas gracias, Dr. Martinez," Juan turned to shake hands. He squared his shoulders in a new way as he went to the waiting room to get Candita. He, Juan Rivera, could help others. What an idea! *¡Qué cosa!* He needed to think that over further.

When Juan told Mama what Dr. Martinez had said

about Candita, Mama slumped down into a chair and laid her head on the kitchen table.

"We cannot do it, Juan. *Es imposible.* And it's so hot in this apartment, if she doesn't go, she'll die. What *will* we do?"

"Don't worry, Mama," Juan told her. *"No es imposible.* When I told the doctor that we cannot do this, he talked about a *friendly town* and promised to arrange it. Then he filled out a printed slip of paper—and you are to go to Casa Central next week to see about it. *No es imposible,* Mama."

Mama got up slowly, and stood at the stove, stirring the *arroz con pollo,* the chicken and rice. Her face had a dead, dull look on it.

"I wouldn't call Chicago a friendly town—not at all," she said. Her eyes were wet with tears.

Suddenly, Juan saw the little mountain church with Brother Mercado standing outside. He remembered his own words: "I will take care of them all." He had not realized then what that promise would mean!

He almost wished he could take back those words! But, of course—¡es imposible!

"And even if I hadn't promised that, I would still be head of the family," he thought to himself. "No one can change that. If only Papa would come back!"

Mama turned to Juan and said, sharply, "You're not listening to a word I say." He came back to the present with a shiver.

"If we can only find Papa," he said. "That is all I ask."

Several days later, Mama herself went to Casa Central. When she came home, she puffed into the kitchen, red-faced with her hurried climb up the three flights of stairs.

"*¡Gracias a Dios!* Thanks be to God!" she exclaimed.

"What is it, Mama?" Alicia asked, as they all crowded round her.

Mama sat down on a chair and kicked off her shoes. "My feet are killing me. And heat up the leftover breakfast coffee, Juan. I need some coffee."

"Well, tell us—what did the people at Casa Central say?" Juan urged as he turned to obey.

"They have already arranged to have Candita go to the country," Mama said, her eyes shining. "It is something they call Friendly Town, with capital letters, you know. And there is a family that will take Candita."

The children were still puzzled. Bit by bit, as Mama talked, they began to understand.

"There are people living not far from Chicago," Mama said. "They want to do something for city children, so they agree to let them stay with them for several weeks.

Dr. Martinez says Candita needs to go, so they have found a family who will take her."

Right then, Candita threw herself down in the middle of the kitchen. She began to scream and drum her heels down on the floor.

"Candita! Stop that!" Mama said.

Candita paid no attention to her. After a bit, when she was no longer crying quite so hard, they could begin to make out a few words.

"I don't want to go to the country, Mama," she hiccuped, finally. "No! Not by myself! I want to stay with you."

"You didn't even listen until I finished!" Mama said sharply. "I know you are too little! That's why I—"

Candita stiffened. "I'm not too little!" she said shortly. "I don't want to go by myself! And, I can't leave Treeta Valeeta."

"Be quiet till Mama finishes," Juan told her.

"The farm where you will be going is a pony farm," Mama said. "They raise them to sell. And they have so many that you can ride them all day, if you want to."

Candita hesitated. A real pony—she'd like that, but, "I don't want to go alone!" she said stubbornly.

"But I told you!" Mama's patience was beginning to wear thin. "You won't be going alone."

They all sat quiet, staring at Mama.

"You must have thought you told us, Mama; but you didn't really," Juan told her.

"I didn't?" Mama looked bewildered. "I started to, then Candita made such a fuss. Well, these people have invited all four of you to come."

They sat there in stunned silence. "All four of us, Mama?" Juan said, at last.

"Yes, yes!" It was like being in Puerto Rico again to see Mama smile the way she always did when she was really pleased about something.

"But you'd be alone yourself, Mama!" Juan said. "I couldn't go away and leave you here all by yourself."

Just then, there was a knock on the door. They were all startled because so few people came to see them.

Juan stood up. "Somebody knocked. But perhaps it is not for us. I will see," he said.

He opened the door and looked out through a narrow crack. "Who is there, please?" he said, because the hall was dark.

"Juan! It *is* Juan!" said a voice that Juan remembered clearly.

"Papa! *¡Gracias a Dios!*"

"*¡Mi familia!*" Papa swept through the door and soon his family were all around him. There were tears of joy,

86

then laughter, then tears again when they heard Papa's story.

When things had quieted down enough so that he could talk, Papa told them about the illness that had kept him from working for so long. He explained how an old Puerto Rican couple, who were lonely for their own family, had taken him in.

"But why didn't you write, Papa?" Juan asked. He had to know the answer to that question.

Papa shook his head. "At first I was too sick and weeks went by when I was not clear of mind. When I grew stronger I kept thinking every day that I might be able to get a job and send some money when I wrote to you. I did not want to ask someone to write until I had money to send, because I felt helpless—a man who could not earn enough to take care of his family!

Juan felt the old lump coming in his throat again. Papa had simply been too discouraged and unhappy to ask someone to write for him. Papa had always been that way—*mañana,* things might be better.

"What does it matter, now?" Mama said. "I will make you some coffee, Papa."

Papa's face lost some of the tired lines. His eyes sparkled a little as he looked at each of the faces of his dear ones.

"But how did you find us, Papa?" Julio asked, suddenly.

"It was when I was getting my strength back after that illness," Papa said. "A neighbor stopped in and told me about Casa Central. He said I could get help there, free of charge. So I went to the clinic."

"Did you go to Dr. Martinez?" Juan asked.

Papa smiled at Juan. "Yes, that is the doctor's name. He told me that a boy named Juan Rivera wanted to see me. He also said that this Juan is a very fine boy—that he had been head of the Rivera family ever since they came to Chicago."

Juan looked down at the scuffed toes of his shoes. So many things raced through his mind. The little home in Puerto Rico. Brother Mercado and the little church. Dr. Martinez and his kindness. Papa sitting there, surrounded by his family, pale and thin but smiling at last, just as he used to do. Maybe he could go to the country along with the rest of the family. Yes, he would ask them at the Casa Central. *They* would help!

"But from now on, I am no longer head of the family, Papa," Juan said, with a wide smile. "You are home, Papa. Welcome home!"

3 Casa Blanca

¡ENTRE!

In this final story, it is Felisa who says, *"¡Entre!"* to you. She and her family have been "following the crops"—that is, they move from place to place, wherever beans, tomatoes, cotton, or other crops are ready for harvest.

There are thousands of farm laborers like Felisa's family in the United States today—not all of them Spanish Americans, of course. Felisa's parents have lived in the United States all their lives, yet Mama never learned to speak English. Her parents came from Mexico when she was a little girl, but in those days there were no school attendance laws and Mama never went to school at all. Besides, every store in the little South Texas town where her family lived had clerks who could speak Spanish.

Papa learned English because he worked for men who

could not speak Spanish. Felisa learned English when she started to school. She had to spend two years in the first grade, because she spent the first six months learning to speak English. Then, too, as a migrant worker's child, she was never able to enter school in September as other children did.

Felisa hated school! She hated it because her family never stayed in one place long enough for her to learn as other boys and girls did. Thanks to a church kindergarten, her little brother, Pedro, would have a better chance in school than Felisa had. He would learn English before he entered first grade and began to read English.

Today many migrant families are settling down in communities, where they live the year round. Families like Felisa's try to earn their own way, but they are paid very little for the work they do. That is why churches want to help them, as new members of the community. They know that having people stay on all year is good for the family and good for the church, too.

There will be fewer migrant workers, like Felisa's family, in the years to come because their work will be done by machines. Machines are beginning to be used to pick cotton, harvest tomatoes, and even dig potatoes. Other machines that may be ready for use soon are onion toppers; planters for celery, tomatoes, and strawberries;

tree shakers for cherries and walnuts; and knockers for almonds and olives. The work of all these machines was previously done by hand.

The Spanish Americans in South Texas are very clever at making use of the things around them. Many of their houses do not have stoves. So, during the day, a fire is built up outdoors. By evening, it has burned down to glowing coals with little smoke. This is shoveled into a washtub and taken indoors. It gives a pleasant heat, a little like a fireplace.

There may be some migrant families who spend part of the year right near your home. Some of them may even be settling down to live the year round in your community. If so, are there things you can do, both at church and at school, to make them feel welcome and wanted?

A Chance for Pedro

Felisa Cruz picked up *The Trail of the Lonesome Pine* and tiptoed to the doorway of the one-room, tar paper shack that was the Cruz home. Ana María, the baby, had just dropped to sleep after crying most of the morning. Four-year-old Pedro was chanting a nonsense song to himself as he played in the shade of the house.

Felisa looked out over the migrant camp—rows and rows of shacks, much like their own, with the open spaces of West Texas beyond them. Out in the middle, a faucet dripped endlessly into a muddy puddle. Down at the far end, a troop of noisy youngsters whooped and howled as their play changed from make-believe wars to real ones and then back to make-believe again. Felisa sighed as she watched them. Pedro was lame so he always played by himself; he would never be able to run and play like that!

TRES CASAS, TRES FAMILIAS

"*¡Uno—dos—tres!* Three ducks in a row," sang Pedro. "Here they go, over the hill."

"*¡Qué cosa!*" Felisa thought to herself. She crept around the corner of the cabin to see what Pedro was doing.

He lay flat on his stomach in the dust with his bare feet waving in the air above his back. He had carried enough water in an old tin can to build a mud "hill." His three "ducks" were three beans in a spoon. Each time, as he sang, "Here they go," the spoon swooped to the other side of the hill.

Felisa clapped both hands over her mouth to keep from laughing. Then she leaned closer. Why, the little monkey! That was one of Mama's spoons he was waving around so carelessly. One of the four spoons that belonged to the Cruz family. Suppose he lost it?

At any other time, Felisa would have swooped down on Pedro and grabbed the spoon without talking about it. Let him yell if he wanted to! She had taken care of him most of his life, so she knew that he'd get over his tantrum as fast as it began.

But today, Ana María was asleep just beyond the tarpaper wall of the house. All the night before and most of the morning, she had tossed and cried. Mama was worried about her.

"Look, Pedro—don't you want me to tell you a story?" Felisa said.

Pedro jumped with surprise and the three beans spilled out into the dust. His lower lip shot out as he glared at Felisa.

Felisa pretended not to notice. She squatted down beside Pedro and leaned against the side of the cabin comfortably, waiting for the moment when she could slip the spoon out of sight without a howl from Pedro.

But Pedro slid around where he could look at Felisa. "Tell about the *casa blanca*," he commanded, as if telling a story had been his idea in the first place.

"The house was *muy poquita*, a very little house," Felisa began. "But it was painted white. And a big—oh, just an e-nor-mous—cottonwood tree grew in the yard."

Pedro closed his eyes. Felisa knew he was trying to "see" the *casa blanca*.

"There were red poinsettias blooming against the outside wall and a bougainvillea vine growing over the front door—oh, such beautiful flowers, Pedro!"

"Posies to pick?" Pedro asked.

"No. Yes. Oh, I don't remember, really. I was so little —just a *chiquita*," Felisa said. "I remember playing in the shade with a little wagon Papa made for me. I loved that wagon!"

"Where was I, 'Lisa?" Pedro asked. "Tell me! Did I ride on the wagon, too? Did I?"

Felisa giggled. "That was before you were born, silly. I was just a little girl when we moved away."

"Why?" Pedro asked. "Why did we move? Tell me, 'Lisa!"

Felisa sighed. She wanted to reread *The Trail of the Lonesome Pine* and now Pedro was asking *hundreds* of questions, as usual. Most days, Felisa had to help out in the fields, while Pedro played nearby. Today, they had been left at home because of Ana María. Felisa loved to read, but there was so little time and no books.

"Well, the rancher Papa worked for sold his ranch," Felisa said. "And now we've been moving and moving ever since, because Papa can't find another job on a ranch."

For a second, Felisa let her mind flit back to the dozens of little cabins that had been home to the Cruz family since then. Some had been terrible. *"¡Es imposible!"* Mama would exclaim when she saw them. Others were sturdy and in good shape. Mama made all of them look like home before long, but then they always moved away again.

"Moving and moving and moving and moving," Pedro

chanted. He rolled over on his back and stared up at the cloudless sky.

A crashing of gears and a squealing of brakes told Felisa that the truck was back from the fields. Mama and Papa were home! Mama came straight toward their cabin. The worried frown on her forehead made her look older than usual. Felisa could tell by the droop of her shoulders how tired she was.

"The baby seems a little better, Mama," Felisa said, as she followed Mama inside. Pedro, using the slow hobbling gait that was his way of walking, hurried in Papa's direction.

"*Gracias a Dios*—her fever is gone!" Mama said, as she put her hand on Ana María's forehead. "I have been so worried, Felisa. It was just so that little Carlota got sick. And Andrés, too. It frightens me."

Carlota and Andrés were Felisa's sister and brother—the two little ones that had lived only a month or two each. Pedro, in spite of his lame feet, was a sturdy little chap.

"You had a better start, Felisa," Mama said with a sigh. "We did not have to take you from place to place before you were old enough to travel. I am afraid for Ana María. She is so little! And now Papa says we leave here tomorrow."

Felisa looked at her mother with a question in her eyes.

"We will go back home now," Mama said. They all called South Texas *home*. "Then you can go to school for a while before Christmas."

"I don't like school, Mama," Felisa said.

Mama's cheerfulness had returned. "Now, now. Of course you do! Besides, it is the only way—so there is no need to speak of it again, Felisa. You must have a chance and school is the only way."

"What about Pedro?" Felisa asked fiercely. "Oh, Mama—what chance will he ever have?"

Mama looked at Felisa for a long minute. Then she pulled out a suitcase and began to pack their clothes.

"There is a chance, *Dios mediante,* if only we could take it!" she said. "The camp nurse said that an operation would probably straighten out Pedro's feet. It should have been done when he was a baby, but it can still be done."

"Then why don't we do it, Mama?" Felisa asked.

"It would take a long time—one year, two years, perhaps. We would need to stay in one place during that time. How could Papa manage? We need to eat. I have thought and thought but I cannot see a way."

Felisa suddenly pulled a box toward her and started to

pile pots and pans into it—this way, that way, without thinking. Tears filled her eyes.

Finally Mama looked over at the box. "*¡Qué cosa!* Not the coffee pot, Felisa! We will need that this evening and tomorrow morning."

Felisa put the coffee pot up on the old black stove again.

To herself she was saying, over and over, "If! If we could only find a way to stay in South Texas—for Pedro's operation."

"Felisa," Mama said, "now I need some water for the coffee. Please hurry. Papa is hungry."

Felisa took the tin pail from her mother's hand and dragged her feet slowly toward the dripping faucet out in the yard.

Was it any use to wish that your family would find a home—a home in South Texas—and never have to move again?

Felisa turned on the faucet and filled the pail as she had dozens of times.

"Dios mediante," she whispered to herself. "Oh, I wish we could—for Pedro's sake!"

Felisa's Dream

By breakfast time the next morning, the Cruz family had packed nearly all of their belongings into the truck. While Felisa and Pedro were drinking their *café con leche,* Mama discovered that one of her spoons had disappeared. None of them had noticed it at suppertime, because they had tamales and tortillas, which they ate with their fingers.

"I know where it is," Felisa said quickly. She jumped up, ran outdoors and dashed around the side of the house.

There was the spoon, where Pedro had left it. And nearby lay Felisa's copy of *The Trail of the Lonesome Pine*—the only book she owned and her dearest treasure. She had reread it so often that she knew whole pages by heart. Scooping up the spoon and the book, she hurried back to the rest.

When Pedro saw her coming in with the spoon, he set up a howl. "My ducks! Where are my ducks?" he sobbed.

Mama and Papa looked at each other. Ducks! What in the world was Pedro talking about?

"Where are the beans, Mama?" Felisa asked in a whisper.

Mama pointed to a half-filled box, waiting for their breakfast dishes. Felisa rummaged through the box for a bit, then slipped three beans into her pocket. She went over to Pedro.

"Here are your ducks, Pedro," she said.

Pedro looked through his fingers before he stopped crying. When Felisa dropped the beans into the palm of his hands, he smiled suddenly.

"How long will it be before he loses them again?" Mama said, in a worried way.

Felisa pulled a wash cloth out of the box of dishes. "Let me fix you a little *casa* for your ducks," she said to Pedro.

It only took a minute to tie opposite corners of the cloth together, forming a little square cage. Pedro laughed and dropped his "ducks" into it. Then he let Felisa tuck the cage safely into his pocket.

"Let's put the box with the beans on top of the rest of

the things," Felisa said to Papa, who was carrying things outside. "Then if he loses them, we can give him others."

"You are good with Pedro, Felisa," Mama said, approvingly. Then she added with a sigh, "No wonder. You've been a mother to him almost as much as I have."

"Come, Mama! Felisa! Pedro! We must get started," Papa called.

They all went out and climbed into the car. Mama sat up front, with Ana María on her lap. Papa was driving. Pedro sat on the seat between them, while Felisa was wedged into a narrow spot that had been left for her on the back seat. One corner of the oil stove jabbed her in the ribs whenever she moved, and the broom slid down and gave her a terrific whack each time Papa rounded a curve. She did not really mind, though. They were going back to South Texas—*home!*

"This time, we'll find a way to stay there!" Felisa thought dreamily. It was easier to feel hopeful in the early morning, with the car tearing off mile after mile of that long ribbon of highway. "Maybe we can really help Pedro's lame feet this year."

Then, as always, Felisa's thoughts turned toward the days that lay ahead. She shuddered as she thought about school.

"I hate school!" she muttered fiercely, under her

breath. She glared at the back of Mama's head for a minute. "Do I really have to go to school?" she asked.

"You certainly do!" Mama told her. "I've told you before—it is the only way. After you grow up, you will be glad we insisted."

"And let's hear no more whining about it," Papa added, sharply.

"Perhaps you will like it better this year," Mama went on, soothingly. "You may find some little girl to be your special friend."

"But I can *never* catch up with the others—never!" Felisa said. "The only girls I ever know follow the crops just as we do. I want a friend who will help me with the lessons that went before."

"But Felisa—you always read as well as the other children in your grade," Mama said. She sounded pleased. "Why do you worry? Even when you start school late each year, you always keep up."

"In reading, yes. In arithmetic, no," Felisa reminded her. But she did feel a little better about school. "Will we live in that same house in Catarina this year, Papa?"

Mama turned her head, to give Felisa a special smile. Pedro and Baby Ana María were fast asleep. The flat Texas countryside whipped past them—miles and miles of emptiness wherever you looked, broken now and then by a wind pump beside a tank, or a cluster of ranch buildings in the distance.

"I did not get a chance to tell you, Felisa. But Papa talked to a man who is from Mathis. He says—"

"Mathis! Where is that?" Felisa asked. Her heart sank into the tips of her shoes. She thought they were going home! She had never heard of Mathis before.

"Don't interrupt Mama when she is speaking, Felisa," Papa said.

"Yes, let me finish. Then you can ask questions." Mama paused to ease Ana María to her other arm. "This man told Papa that he can get work in Mathis. And there is a children's hospital not too far away. We hope something can be done for Pedro at last."

Felisa stared at Mama. "Do you really think so?" she whispered.

"We plan to try," Papa said quietly.

Felisa couldn't talk past the lump in her throat. She wanted to go back to Catarina—to go *home*. It was bad enough to think about starting school there, and it would be much worse anywhere else.

But then she thought about Pedro, playing in the shade of the cabin with his "ducks" while other children his age dashed in and out of the mesquite bushes and played running games on sturdy little legs.

Of course, they should go to Mathis. Felisa admitted that to herself with a sigh so deep that Mama heard her up front.

"It may not be as bad as you think," Mama said. "Life is like a seesaw, you know. When one side goes down, the other goes up. Sometimes there are good things that balance out the bad ones."

During the days that followed, Felisa often thought about what Mama had said. Coming to Mathis really did bring a lot of ups and downs to the Cruz family.

"We live in a house with two rooms instead of just one—*bueno!*" Felisa said. "But it was the dirtiest of them all when we first came—*malo*. Mama has cleaned it up for us so that it looks like home—*bueno*. It is far from the stores and from school—*malo*. We have a live oak tree in the back yard—*bueno*."

Felisa paused in her counting to look out through the back door. Pedro was playing under the live oak tree, using a string of tin cans for a train. They were held together by a rubber band, bits of string, and some wire— things he had collected from among the junk that was scattered everywhere. Mama had cleaned up the inside of the house, but no one had yet had time to work on the outside. Papa was already busy picking vegetables on a nearby truck farm.

"That tree is certainly *bueno*," Felisa thought. "But tomorrow I must go to school—that is *malo*. ¡*Muy malo!*"

Next morning, Felisa started off to school with dragging footsteps. After she arrived, she stood in the hall for a while. The fluttery feeling in her chest seemed to choke her.

So many rooms—so many grades! Which one was hers? Then she noticed signs on the doors. Grade Four. Grade Five. Ah, yes—there it was—Grade Six. Her hand was trembling as she reached for the doorknob.

She tried to slip in unnoticed, but as soon as she stepped inside, the buzz of talk died away. Everybody stared as Felisa walked to the teacher's desk. Later on, there would be many newcomers, but just then Felisa was the only one.

Felisa could feel eyes boring into her back as she said, in a small voice, "My name is Felisa Cruz."

She took a timid look around the room, but there were eyes everywhere. She dropped her own, but not before she had a chance to see several empty desks by the window. Sometimes, the room had every desk filled; then the teacher had to supply a table and chair, while Felisa stood in full sight of everybody, waiting.

Today, Miss Mills motioned her to a desk almost immediately. "You will sit next to Manuela Ortiz," she said.

"She will help you get settled and look out for you today —won't you, Manuela?"

Felisa sneaked a look at Manuela and saw big brown eyes looking at her over the top of a spelling book. They felt stiff toward each other at first, but at recess they suddenly began to talk.

From then on, the Cruz family heard about Manuela Ortiz every day. Felisa said, "Manuela says—" so often that Papa teased her about being Manuela's echo.

"Manuela says her papa has a ranch," Felisa reported. And "Manuela says she has read *Peter Pan* twelve times. She borrowed *The Trail of the Lonesome Pine*, but she says there are too many hard words in it." And again— "Manuela says she goes to church every Sunday with her Papa and Mama and her little sister, María. Mama, why don't we go to church like Manuela's family?"

Then one evening, Felisa rushed home and tossed her books on the table. "Mama, Mama! Just listen to this! Manuela wants me to come and visit her this weekend. She wants me to stay over night."

"Now, just one little minute," Mama said. The corners of her mouth turned down as her forehead made little frown-wrinkles. "Señor Ortiz is a big rancher. Are you sure Manuela had her parents' permission before she asked you?"

"Here is a note from Señora Ortiz." Felisa fished the battered bit of paper out of her pocket and gave it to Mama. "Manuela says they have many friends who follow the crops. She wants me to come on Saturday. Then they will bring me to town with them when they come to church on Sunday. And Mama—"

"Yes, Felisa?"

"Manuela wants me to go to church with her. Then her Papa will bring me home afterwards. May I, Mama? Please, may I?"

Mama stared straight ahead for a minute. "I know we have not been going to church as we should," she admitted with a sigh.

"When I was a little girl, we went every Sunday."

Mama nodded. "Then we started following the crops. That made it hard. Everything's hard. Now stop chattering and let me see what Señora Ortiz says."

When Mama finished reading, she looked at Felisa. "Her words are very kind," she said. "Their church is not our church, of course."

"Which is our church?" Felisa asked. She liked to be matter of fact. "We don't really have a church, do we?"

Mama's face cleared. "Well, you are right, Felisa. And these people are kind, so we will accept their kindness."

"¡Bueno! ¡Bueno!" Felisa sang. "Now the seesaw is

going up, Mama. Manuela told me something else. She said—" Felisa looked meaningly at Pedro, crouched under the table playing with Mama's clothespins. Perhaps she ought to wait to mention it until she and Mama were alone, but when would that be?

"Pedro, don't you want to play outside for a while?" she said, with a look at Mama.

Pedro looked up quickly. "No. Go away!" he said.

"Don't be so stubborn, Pedro!" Felisa said.

"Now, Felisa!" Mama cautioned.

"Well, I didn't want him to be disappointed, but I guess he'll just have to take his chance. Anyway, Manuela told me about the kindergarten her church has for little children like Pedro. They learn to speak English. Then, when they start to school, they understand what the teacher says and can learn their lessons along with the others."

"We had better wait and see," Mama said. "If we take Pedro to that clinic at the Children's Hospital, he won't be able to go to kindergarten."

Pedro's chin jutted out, at its worst angle. "I want to go!" he said. "Mama! Let me! I want to!"

Felisa and Mama looked at each other helplessly. Pedro always got his own way when he acted like that.

"We should not give in to him so much," Mama said

114

with a sigh. "But because of his lame feet, it is hard not to."

"His feet and his stubbornness," Felisa muttered. Then she replied, "But even if he couldn't go every day, he could go sometimes. Manuela says there are toys and puzzles and tractors and blocks. It will not matter so much if Pedro cannot run and jump like the rest."

"Papa had better see about it," Mama agreed. "Now, Pedro—that is enough! *¡Cuidado!* Be careful. Or a rooster will come and sit on your lip! We will wait and see what Papa says."

Saturday came at last and Felisa's visit at the Ortiz ranch was everything she had dreamed it would be. There were the big trees around the sprawling white ranch house. The board fences were painted white. There were the cattle in corrals, and horses tossing their heads beyond the high gate.

"It is as I remember," Felisa said. "Oh, Manuela, it is exactly the same!"

"What do you mean?" Manuela asked. "It can't be 'exactly the same.' You've never been here before, Felisa!"

"Papa used to work on a ranch near Catarina," Felisa explained. "We lived in a little house out there. Of course, it wasn't this ranch; I know that! But ranches are much alike, you know. Except that your house is much bigger than ours was, it's as if I have been here before."

"We'll pretend that you're my sister," Manuela said. "Tonight, you'll sleep in the other twin bed in my room. From now on, we will call it Felisa's bed. Now come on! We have puppies at the barn. They're brown and white and awfully cute. Supper will be late because of Papa."

"Your Papa is away?" Felisa asked.

"No, he isn't. But right now, he is short one man on the ranch, so he has to work very hard. Mama doesn't like it. She hopes he will get someone soon, but Papa insists he won't take a man without experience."

"He needs a man, you say?" Felisa asked. Her thoughts were racing ahead.

"Yes," said Manuela. " 'Never again a man without experience!' Papa said, and banged his fist on the table. I think it was because of Sanchez, the man he had before. He sometimes acted as if he were walking around half-asleep, so Papa had to let him go."

Felisa didn't seem to hear her. She was staring straight ahead, thinking hard. Papa had worked on a ranch once upon a time. Señor Ortiz needed a man with experience. If Papa could get that job, the Cruz family could stay at Mathis all year round. They could take Pedro to the clinic and have his feet straightened. She and Manuela could go to school together and play together. Next year,

Felisa could start school right on the very first day—

Manuela twitched at Felisa's sleeve. "Come on! Wake up! Let's go see the puppies."

Felisa's dream faded. She jumped up. She had a friend all her own and together they raced off to the barn.

Under the Live Oak Tree

When Felisa burst into the Cruz cabin after church the next day, the whole family was there. During the night a norther had blown into South Texas bringing cold weather with it. So Papa had built a fire outdoors in the forenoon and then let it burn down. After that, he shoveled the hot coals into an old tub and brought it indoors. It made a pleasant heat with little smoke, like a fireplace–although Felisa noticed that, as usual, she was roasting on one side and freezing on the other.

Mama sat beside the washtub stove, holding Ana María. Papa had settled himself on a rickety chair left there by the Gomez family and put his stocking-feet up on a keg. He was tired. Once in a while, his head nodded, then he jerked awake again. Pedro had an old syrup bucket full of water and was fishing in it with a twig for his pole, a string for a line, and a paper clip for a hook.

"Oh, Mama! Papa!" Felisa started talking as soon as she opened the door. "Just think! Manuela's dog has puppies. They are so cute!"

"Did you say "thank you" to Señora Ortiz?" Mama asked.

"Yes—no. Oh, I don't remember." Felisa dropped several books on the table. There was so much to talk about and Mama would ask that! "At the church, there's a library. Manuela says I can check out two books every Saturday. See! I got *Corn Farm Boy* for myself—and here is one for Pedro with pictures!"

Felisa held up the book and read the title to Mama: *Make Way for Ducklings.*

Mama looked worried. "I hope you will take good care of them, Felisa. If you lose one or spoil any pages, we'll have to pay. And books cost—oh, ever so much money. Besides, the book for Pedro is in English."

"I'll translate it for him," Felisa promised. "The pictures tell the story, anyway. And listen, Mama, the people at church were all so friendly. When the pastor shook hands with me, he said, 'So you are the little newcomer. I hope you will be happy here in Mathis!' Just as if he knew about us already."

Mama and Papa exchanged glances. "Well, Felisa," Mama began, but just then Pedro jumped up.

"Felisa! I'm going to the little school!" he shouted.

"¡*Qué cosa!* What is he talking about, Mama?"

Pedro started to shuffle around the little room, chanting to himself. "I'm going to the little school *mañana!* I'm going to the little school *mañana!*

"You're not the only one who has news, Felisa," Mama said. "On Saturday, Miss Anderson—she teaches at that kindergarten Manuela was talking about—came to see us. Señora Ortiz had spoken to her. People here are very kind.

Mama stopped to wipe her eyes on one corner of her apron. Then she went on. "She says that she does not really have room for another pupil. And Pedro is not supposed to go until he is five. But since he will soon be old enough, she will make a place for him. And she also says that she knows a family from the church that goes to the children's clinic once a month because their child has had polio. She will see whether Pedro and I can go with them—that way Papa won't have to miss any work. And maybe the next time, Papa can drive."

For a minute, Felisa was speechless. Things were happening too fast for her!

"When Miss Anderson came, I was ashamed," Mama said. "I told her we had not had time to clean up outside yet. She said it was too bad that the Gomez family left

120

this cabin so dirty—with trash everywhere, inside and out. She will ask Señor Ortiz to bring his truck next Saturday and then Papa can load the trash on it, and haul it to the dump."

Felisa sat down on an upturned apple crate. "I wonder why they bother," she said. She talked softly, as if she were saying it to herself. "I wonder why—"

"I wouldn't worry about that," Papa said. "We have had many hard things to bear during these past years. *Gracias a Dios* that now someone will help us."

"I talked to Miss Anderson about that," Mama said. "She told me that many people here follow the crops, as we do. Or if they don't now, they did at one time. 'We have all been helped ourselves,' she said. 'Because we are thankful to God, we want to help others.' "

For a minute, Papa's face clouded. "I wish we *could* stay here," he said. "But soon the work will run out—"

"Oh, Papa!" Felisa jumped up again. "Listen! Señor Ortiz needs another man on his ranch. He wants a man who knows about cattle. Papa, do you suppose maybe—"

Papa looked straight at Felisa. "Is this true? Are you sure this is not just little girls' chatter?"

"Manuela said her father hit the table with his fist—so! He said he would never hire anyone again who did not have experience. But her mama worries because

Señor Ortiz works so hard now that he has to work alone."

"That sounds like the real thing," Papa said. "We must see about this. Yes—we certainly must see about this."

He got up and went outdoors. In a few minutes, they heard him drive away. And several hours later, when he came back, Felisa could tell by the very way Papa walked, and his smile, that he had the job. She had helped Papa find a job—and, *gracias a Dios,* a stay-in-one-place job!

A few days later, on Saturday morning, Señor Ortiz and Manuela drove up to the front door of the Cruz home in his truck. As soon as it stopped, Manuela hopped out and ran for the house. She stopped to talk to Pedro in the yard as Felisa came out to meet her.

"Do you like the little school, Pedro?" Manuela asked.

Pedro nodded his head. "We have real trucks," he said. "I like real trucks."

Manuela looked at Felisa. "What does he mean?"

"That's his *truck* here at home," Felisa explained, pointing to a wood block. Papa had nailed on wheels made of bottle caps and sketched in windows and doors with a bit of charcoal.

"He's learning English at kindergarten, too," Felisa added, proudly. "Say something in English, Pedro."

"No—no!" Pedro said sharply.

Manuela and Felisa both laughed. "Well, *no* is the

same in both languages, so he spoke English without knowing it. But he really can say a few sentences already. He's just too stubborn to do it right now."

The men were loading trash on the truck, so the girls went to watch. Pedro tagged along.

"There are a *million* tin cans," Manuela said.

"I'd say *two million*," Felisa corrected her. "But what does it matter—as long as they get hauled away?"

Every so often, someone unearthed something they could use. An old dishpan, less battered than the one Mama was using. A pancake turner. Three spoons. A frying pan that was not too rusty. A dozen big flower pots.

"It's a wonder these weren't broken," Felisa said.

They saved everything that could possibly be used. Then, as soon as the yard was cleared, the men drove off to the dump. Mama gave Felisa the broom and told her to start sweeping. Carefully, she swept off the upper layer of the dust from the bone-hard clay underneath.

When the truck came back, Pedro noticed that there was a big bag, and a small box, in the back of the truck.

"What is it, Papa?" he asked, hobbling out to the truck as fast as he could. Papa was saying *gracias* to Señor Ortiz and paid no attention, so Pedro kept on repeating his question. "What is it, Papa?"

Felisa and Manuela came running, too. They watched

Papa lift the big bag, and a wide brush, from the truck
Then he took out the small box.

"Just one little minute," said Papa, smiling.

"We must go home now, Manuela," Señor Ortiz said.

"I'll tell you about it tomorrow at church," Felisa
shouted. "Good-bye Manuela!"

By the time she got back, Papa had already dumped
some white powder into an old bucket. He added water
and began to stir it round and round.

After it was thoroughly mixed, he brought an apple
crate from inside the house. By stepping on it, he could
just reach the eaves with his brush. He slapped it up and
down, up and down, leaving a wide grey strip.

"Papa! Are you painting it grey?" Felisa demanded.

"It's whitewash," Papa explained. "It will dry white—
very white. We'd feel more at home in a white house!"

In a couple of hours, the job was finished. Even the
bricks that lined the path to the street and the tree trunk
(as high as Papa could reach) gleamed white and clean.
The clay flower pots, no longer red but white, stood beside the front door, waiting for flowers. And the strange
little box—it stood alone, white as could be.

"Señor Ortiz has promised us some geranium slips,"
said Papa, smiling. Then he reached into his pocket and
brought out a tiny can of paint. "And now, Felisa, bring

me a twig from the live oak tree."

Felisa watched, too excited to move, as Papa slowly pried open the little can. Then in a flash she was off, and back—with a twig for mixing paint. *Red* paint!

As the children watched, Papa stirred the paint. Then he took the small white box and slowly painted on it in red letters: RICARDO CRUZ.

"A *mailbox!* Why, that's only for people who stay in one place!" thought Felisa. And the house—well, it was the *casa blanca* of her stories. Almost, at least. Pedro came and slipped his hand into hers.

"Once upon a time, there was a white house under a big tree," Felisa said to him.

"Tell me the rest of the story!" Pedro begged.

Felisa scarcely heard him. Papa had a job so now they could stay in Mathis as long as they wanted to. Tomorrow, the Cruz family would all go to church—she had heard Papa tell Señor Ortiz so.

At the clinic that week, the doctor had said Pedro would walk someday. It would take a long time, but what did that matter?

Felisa clasped Pedro's hand tightly in hers. By half-closing her eyes, she could see him walking straight and tall, without any limp or shuffle, up the path to the *casa blanca* under the live oak tree.

Date Loaned

The
in 1

Man
Leba
Text
Typ

Demco 38-295